GARFIELD

Classics

Volume Four

MY FOURTH CLASSIC COLLECTION
CONTAINS:

WE LOVE YOU TOO

HERE WE GO AGAIN

LIFE AND LASAGNE

JIM DAVIS

ℛℛ

This edition first published by
Ravette Publishing 1999

Printed and bound in Great Britain
for Ravette Publishing Limited,
Unit 3, Tristar Centre,
Star Road, Partridge Green,
West Sussex RH13 8RA
by Cox & Wyman Ltd, Reading, Berkshire

ISBN: 1 85304 997 2

Garfield
We Love You Too

JIM DAVIS

5-12

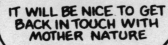

CLICK

ARRGH!

JIM DAVIS

SORRY, GARFIELD

I WISH YOU'D WARN ME

© 1981 United Feature Syndicate, Inc.

10-24

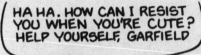

HA HA. HOW CAN I RESIST YOU WHEN YOU'RE CUTE? HELP YOURSELF, GARFIELD

JIM DAVIS

A FOOL AND HIS LASAGNA ARE SOON PARTED

© 1981 United Feature Syndicate, Inc.

© 1981 United Feature Syndicate, Inc.

I CAN'T REACH THAT PIE, NERMAL. WHAT SAY WE TEAM UP?

© 1982 United Feature Syndicate, Inc.   JIM DAVIS

10-28

© 1984 United Feature Syndicate, Inc.

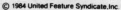

© 1984 United Feature Syndicate, Inc.

JIM DAVIS   8-22

© 1984 United Feature Syndicate, Inc.

© 1984 United Feature Syndicate, Inc. JIM DAVIS

© 1984 United Feature Syndicate, Inc.

© 1984 United Feature Syndicate, Inc.

© 1984 United Feature Syndicate, Inc.

10-18

© 1964 United Feature Syndicate, Inc.

© 1984 United Feature Syndicate, Inc.

© 1984 United Feature Syndicate, Inc.

© 1984 United Feature Syndicate, Inc.

© 1984 United Feature Syndicate, Inc.

© 1984 United Feature Syndicate, Inc.

SLUP!

THAT WAS MY LAST CUP OF COFFEE!

I SPILLED SOME. YOU CAN SUCK IT OUT OF MY SWEATER

© 1985 United Feature Syndicate, Inc.

© 1985 United Feature Syndicate, Inc.

10-8   JIM DAVIS

I HATE THAT WHEN THE COASTER STICKS TO MY GLASS THEN FALLS ONTO THE TABLE!

GAHFIELD, CUD I HAFF A WUD WIF YOU?

© 1985 United Feature Syndicate, Inc.

© 1985 United Feature Syndicate, Inc.

© 1985 United Feature Syndicate, Inc.

© 1985 United Feature Syndicate, Inc

© 1985 United Feature Syndicate, Inc

© 1985 United Feature Syndicate Inc

© 1985 United Feature Syndicate, Inc.

© 1985 United Feature Syndicate, Inc

© 1985 United Feature Syndicate, Inc.

© 1985 United Feature Syndicate, Inc.

© 1985 United Feature Syndicate, Inc.

© 1985 United Feature Syndicate, Inc.

© 1985 United Feature Syndicate, Inc

SURPRISE!

© 1985 United Feature Syndicate, Inc.

HAPPY BIRTHDAY, GARFIELD!

I HAD A FEELING THIS WAS COMING

© 1985 United Feature Syndicate Inc

© 1985 United Feature Syndicate, Inc.

© 1985 United Feature Syndicate inc.

© 1985 United Feature Syndicate, Inc.

5-16

THAT'S A PRETTY FUNKY DANCE, GARFIELD. SHOW ME HOW YOU DO IT

© 1985 United Feature Syndicate, Inc.

FIRST, FIND A BUR IN YOUR SANDBOX

JIM DAVIS

© 1985 United Feature Syndicate, Inc.

© 1985 United Feature Syndicate, Inc.

© 1985 United Feature Syndicate, Inc

© 1985 United Feature Syndicate, Inc

© 1985 United Feature Syndicate, Inc.

JIM DAVPS

10-19

© 1985 United Feature Syndicate Inc

© 1985 United Feature Syndicate, Inc.

Garfield

Life and Lasagne

JIM DAVIS   ℛℛ

© 1985 United Feature Syndicate, Inc.

© 1985 United Feature Syndicate, Inc.

© 1985 United Feature Syndicate, Inc.

© 1985 United Feature Syndicate, Inc.

© 1985 United Feature Syndicate, Inc.

© 1985 United Feature Syndicate,Inc

© 1985 United Feature Syndicate, Inc.

10-22

© 1985 United Feature Syndicate, Inc.

© 1985 United Feature Syndicate, Inc.

© 1985 United Feature Syndicate, Inc.

4-8　JIM DAVIS

© 1985 United Feature Syndicate, Inc.

I'VE BEEN AWAKE ONE SECOND AND ALREADY MY DAY IS RUINED

© 1985 United Feature Syndicate, Inc.

© 1985 United Feature Syndicate, Inc.

© 1985 United Feature Syndicate, Inc.

5-2

© 1985 United Feature Syndicate,Inc.

KISS

PETS ALWAYS SENSE WHEN YOU'RE GOING TO THE GROCERY

BUY ME A STEAK

© 1985 United Feature Syndicate, Inc.

© 1985 United Feature Syndicate, Inc.

© 1985 United Feature Syndicate, Inc

ZIP

© 1985 United Feature Syndicate, Inc.

OTHER GARFIELD BOOKS AVAILABLE

Pocket Books @ £2.99 each	ISBN
Flying High	1 85304 043 6
A Gift For You	1 85304 190 4
The Gladiator	1 85304 941 7
Going Places	1 85304 242 0
Great Impressions	1 85304 191 2
Hangs On	1 85304 784 8
Happy Landings	1 85304 105 X
Here We Go Again	0 948456 10 8
In The Pink	0 948456 67 1
In Training	1 85304 785 6
The Irresistible	1 85304 940 9
Just Good Friends	0 948456 68 X
Le Mangnifique!	1 85304 243 9
Let's Party	1 85304 906 9
On The Right Track	1 85304 907 7
On Top Of The World	1 85304 104 1
Pick Of The Bunch	1 85304 258 7
The Reluctant Romeo	1 85304 391 5
Says It With Flowers	1 85304 316 8
Show At First Sight	1 85304 990 5
Stikes Again	0 906710 62 6
To Eat, Or Not To Eat?:	1 85304 991 3
Wave Rebel	1 85304 317 6
With Love From Me To You	1 85304 392 3
(available Feb 2000)	
Double Trouble	1 84161 008 9
Byte Me	1 84161 009 7

Theme Books @ £3.99 each	
Guide to Behaving Badly	1 85304 892 5
Guide to Healthy Living	1 85304 972 7
Guide to Insults	1 85304 895 X
Guide to Pigging Out	1 85304 893 3
Guide to Romance	1 85304 894 1
Guide to Successful Living	1 85304 973 5

(available Sept '99)	
Guide to Creatures Great and Small	1 85304 998 0
Guide to The Seasons	1 85304 999 9

Classics @ £4.99 each   ISBN
Volume One   1 85304 970 0
Volume Two   1 85304 971 9
Volume Three   1 85304 996 4

Miscellaneous
Garfield Treasury   £9.99   1 85304 975 1

Garfield Address & Birthday   1 85304 918 2
Book Gift Set   £7.99 inc VAT

Garfield 21st Birthday   1 85304 995 6
Celebration Book   £9.99

All Garfield books are available at your local bookshop or from the address below.
Just tick the titles required and send the form with your payment to:-

B.B.C.S., P.O. BOX 941, HULL, NORTH HUMBERSIDE HU1 3YQ
24 Hour Telephone Credit Card Line 01482 224626
Prices and availability are subject to change without notice.
Please enclose a cheque or postal order made payable to B.B.C.S. to the value of
the cover price of the book and allow the following for postage and packing:

U.K. & B.F.P.O.:	£1.95 (weight up to 1kg)	3-day delivery
	£2.95 (weight up to 1kg up to 20kg)	3-day delivery
	£4.95 (weight up to 20kg)	next day delivery
EU & Eire: Surface Mail	£2.50 for first book & £1.50 for subsequent books	
Airmail	£4.00 for first book & £2.50 for subsequent books	
USA: Surface Mail	£4.50 for first book & £2.50 for subsequent books	
Airmail	£7.50 for first book & £3.50 for subsequent books	
Rest of Surface Mail	£6.00 for first book & £3.50 for subsequent books	
The World Airmail	£10.00 for first book & £4.50 for subsequent books	

Name . . . .

Address . . . .

. . . .

. . . .

Cards accepted: Visa, Mastercard, Switch, Delta, American Express

Expiry Date . . . . Signature . . . .